# the mountains

Translation: Jean Grasso Fitzpatrick

First English language edition published
1986 by Barron's Educational Series, Inc.

© Parramón Ediciones, S.A., 1986

The title of the Spanish edition is *la montaña*

All inquiries should be addressed to:
Barron's Educational Series, Inc.
113 Crossways Park Drive
Woodbury, New York 11797

International Standard Book No.
Paper: 0-8120-3698-0
Hardcover: 0-8120-5746-5

**Library of Congress Cataloging-in-Publication Data**

Rius, María.
   Let's discover the mountains.

   (Let's discover series)
   Translation of: *La Montaña.*
   Summary: Describes mountains, the plants and
animals that live on them, and the many pleasures
they offer.
   1. Mountains—Juvenile literature. [1. Moun-
tains]
I. Parramon, José María. II. Title. III. Series.
GB512.R5813   1986   910'.09143   86-7990
ISBN 0-8120-5746-5          JE   Ohio/Mi
ISBN 0-8120-3698-0 (pbk.)       8.29

Register Book Number: 785
Legal Deposit: B-24.424-86

Printed in Spain by Sirven Grafic, S.A.
Gran Vía, 754 - 08013 Barcelona

# let's discover
# the mountains

## María Rius
## J. M. Parramón

CHILDRENS PRESS CHOICE

A Barron's title selected for educational distribution
ISBN 0-516-08672-3

When everything around you seems
to go on for as far as your eye can see...

and there is peace and silence.

When the clouds and the sky
seem to be much closer…

and, from up high, you can see
deep valleys…

and where the rivers begin...

and eagles flying, and deer running by you.

When you go on long hikes

and see plants and flowers,
trees and animals…

beautiful lakes with crystal clear water…

and small towns with pointed bell-towers.

When the cold is crisp, and the winds are very strong,

and you can enjoy the endless snow....

You are in the mountains!

# THE MOUNTAINS

## GUIDE FOR PARENTS AND TEACHERS

### What is a mountain?

If you look up *mountain* in the dictionary, it may say "...all land above thirteen thousand feet." But for people who visit the mountains, and know them and love them, that definition isn't really good enough. The mountains are, for many young and not so young people, a place for recreation and fun; but they also have a deeper meaning. The mountain's silence, lovely landscapes, and solitude bring peace and serenity to people's lives in a way that nothing else can.

### Geographic description

Some mountains are single and isolated, while others are grouped together forming ranges. Mountain ranges sometimes link together to form chains. By height, mountains can be classified in three ways: a high mountain (more than 7,500 feet) is ideal for winter sports like skiing; a medium-sized mountain is 3,000 to 7,500 feet high; and a low mountain is no higher than 3,000 feet.

### Climate and plant life

As you go up a mountain, every 330 feet the temperature drops about one degree. This, along with the strong winds caused by sheer drops and steep cliffs sometimes makes the climate on a mountain very uncomfortable. Both the severe weather and the altitude affect growing things such as trees and shrubs. On the lower slopes there are dense woods that get plenty of water from the torrents and rivers that start to flow with the spring thaw; but higher up there are fewer trees, and the mountains are covered with grassy pastureland.

### Hill-walking and mountain climbing

People have always been powerfully attracted to mountains. Since the earliest times, climbers have tried to scale even the highest peaks. In 1336, the Italian poet Petrarch, along with some of his friends, reached the top of Mount Ventoux. But mountain climbing as a sport really began in the middle of the eighteenth century. That's when H. B. Saussure began to write about the methods of climbing mountains. Most of the summits had already been climbed between 1850 and 1865, which was the year that the first tragedy in mountain climbing occurred. While descending Mount Cervino, four mountaineers died. After this, mountaineering became known as a dangerous sport, but that did not prevent it from attracting a growing number of followers.

## Hiking

Since the 1890's, the sport of mountain climbing also came to include the hobby of hiking. Hiking is usually done for cultural or scientific reasons. Groups of young people like to get together because they want to enjoy nature, get to know the countryside, and have a good time with their friends. Long walks and camping trips make for lasting friendships that people enjoy all the more because they also feel close to nature and the world around them.

## Life in the mountains

Living in the mountains is harder than living on lower ground. The climate, the steep slopes, the avalanches, and the heavy snowfalls are difficult to deal with. But to the first people who settled in the mountains, the abundance of game made up for all the problems. Centuries later, the fact that some mountains were almost impossible to climb made them useful for defense and protection. Today, not many people live in the mountains permanently, but there are still small towns near forest developments, hydroelectric plants, winter sports centers, and tourist areas.

**The mountains have always protected us, offering refuge in time of danger because of their inaccessible height, and enriching our spirits by permitting us to live in contact with nature and share this experience with other mountaineers.**